GW00585693

Scan this QR code to buy the physical Manta Planner

Find tips, training, and a community at
www.mantaplanner.com

To provide any feedback
Email samiradaswani@gmail.com

© Samira Daswani 2020

THE MANTA PLANNER

The manta ray is an elegant animal that has learned how to glide through the many conditions of the ocean. It has learned how to harness the energy from its environment and glide through the ever changing ocean environment. The manta ray extends it's wings , graciously flies through even tumultuous waters. The manta ray became a source of inspiration for my journey through cancer.

I created the planner while undergoing chemotherapy for breast cancer. I was diagnosed a few weeks after my 30th birthday. Like many other cancer patients, the journey through diagnosis, treatment and survivorship was overwhelming, with good days and some terrible ones.

I realized that there was no one place to keep my notes, track my symptoms, planner my emotions, and coordinate the many things that this path included. I found myself in many appointments trying to remember what happened when, and wishing I had kept better notes.

I designed it for us. On one of those days, the receptionist at the cancer clinic offered me a hand-knitted hat that another patient had made for us. It brightened my day, and gave me something I used for the next many months. Being diagnosed with cancer brought with it membership to this club of other cancer patients. I don't knit, but I am a designer who works in the healthcare space. This planner is my way of giving back to this community.

I hope that this planner makes life just a little bit easier during this journey. If you have any thoughts on the planner, or want to simply chat, please do reach out to me at samira@mantacares.com.

THIS PLANNER BELONGS TO

CONTENTS

This treatment planner is designed to help patients & caregivers along this journey. It has modules to capture notes from doctor appointments, results from tests, treatment plans, medication management, and symptom tracking. Most importantly, the planner is designed to help you navigate to better health. The planner has sections to help you recall what you are grateful for, and what your are hopeful for.

This Planner includes the following modules:

IMPORTANT CONTACTS

Capture important contact information of your care team - primary oncologist, primary physician, and nurses.

NAME ______________________________

EMAIL ______________________________

PHONE ______________________________

FAX ______________________________

NAME ______________________________

EMAIL ______________________________

PHONE ______________________________

FAX ______________________________

NAME ______________________________

EMAIL ______________________________

PHONE ______________________________

FAX ______________________________

IMPORTANT INFORMATION

Capture important contact information of your care team - primary oncologist, primary physician, and nurses.

INSURANCE INFORMATION

INSURANCE ____________________

MEMBER ID ____________________

GROUP ID ____________________

CONTACT ____________________

CAREGIVER INFORMATION

NAME ____________________

EMAIL ____________________

PHONE ____________________

FAX ____________________

CAREGIVER INFORMATION

NAME ____________________

EMAIL ____________________

PHONE ____________________

FAX ____________________

DIAGNOSIS

This section of the planner is meant to provide one place to capture the highlights of your diagnostic plan. If your journey was anything like mine, the period of diagnosis of cancer is an incredibly stressful one. The uncertainty, the overwhelming nature of informaton being thrown at you and the coordination to get it all done is difficult. This section of the planner has structured sections to capture the takeaways from each of the tests done.

IMAGING

This could include ultrasound, MRI, CT scans, PET scans, echocardiograms etc.

PROCEDURES

This often includes a biopsy (sometimes multiple), placing a port for infusion etc.

GENETICS

Sometimes genetic testing can be meaningful in achieving a proper diagnosis.

BLOOD

Oh so many blood tests! There maybe certain markers in your blood that your physician might want to monitor.

QUESTIONS TO HELP YOU PLAN

What additional tests should I be doing?

Developing your diagnosis often includes taking a number of tests, including imaging studies, blood tests, some procedures like a biopsy. Ask your doctor which tests are most important for you to do. Remember to ask what order the tests should be done in as well.

What are the critical milestones along this path?

Often times your prognosis, i.e., the outcome of the treatment, can be determined at various milestones along this journey. Asking your doctor what those milestones could help develop your diagnosis and treatment plan.

Can we get prior authorization for these tests?

Early on in the journey of cancer, often insurance coverage comes up. As a general rule of thumb asking for prior authorization for the tests coming up helps smooth the rails for insurance logistics.

Should I be doing any genetic testing?

Depending on your type of cancer, genetic testing may be a critical part of confirming your diagnosis. Asking your oncologist about this is helpful.

Which tests are the most senstive for my cancer?

Depending on your type and stage of cancer, different testing modalities become more critical. Asking your clinician which tests are most critical to monitoring your cancer can be helpful.

How often should I be doing these tests?

Asking your oncologist about which tests will be done on an ongoing basis, such as, which tests will be repeated and when along the journey you are embarking.

INITIAL DIAGNOSIS

01	TYPE

02	STAGE

03	DETAILS

04	TESTS REMAINING

05 **POTENTIAL OUTCOMES**

06 **OPEN QUESTIONS**

UPDATED DIAGNOSIS

01 TYPE

02 STAGE

03 DETAILS

04 POTENTIAL OUTCOMES

05 TESTS REMAINING

06 FINAL DIAGNOSES

ONGOING TESTS

TEST NAME

FREQUENCY

TEST NAME

FREQUENCY

TEST NAME

FREQUENCY

TEST NAME

FREQUENCY

TEST NAME

FREQUENCY

TEST NAME

FREQUENCY

TREATMENT PLAN

This section of the planner is meant to provide one place to capture the highlights of your diagnostic plan. If your journey was anything like mine, the period of diagnosis of cancer is an incredibly stressful one. The uncertainty, the overwhelming nature of informaton being thrown at you and the coordination to get it all done is difficult. This section of the planner has structured sections to capture the takeaways from each of the tests done.

SURGERY

This could include surgical removal of your tumor, a transplant or additional invasive surgical procedures.

CHEMOTHERAPY

Based on your particular cancer, there might be systemic treatment such as chemotherapy.

RADIATION THERAPY

You might have radiation therapy included in your overall treatment plan.

TARGETED THERAPY

Some cancer treatment plans include targeted treatment, such as Herceptin for breast cancer.

QUESTIONS TO HELP YOU PLAN

What's the standard of care?

You can ask your doctor what is the standard of care for your type of cancer for most people in your demographic band. This does not mean that it is the best plan for you. Understanding standard of care is still helpful in evaluating your options. This includes both which treatment modules and the order in which they are administered.

What are the critical milestones along this plan?

Often times your prognosis, i.e., the guess on the outcome of the treatment, can be determined at various milestones along this journey. Asking your doctor what those milestones could help develop your treatment plan.

What is the overall and progress-free outcomes?

Your journey is unique. If you are like me, understanding the data of my cancer, helped me gain perspective. Cancer outcomes are determined across 2 categories: overall survival, and progression free survival. It's important to ask your doctor what the data suggests. Remember, this data is often not adjusted to reflect your specific case.

If chemo, adjuvant or neo-adjuvant?

If chemotherapy is a part of your plan, it's sometimes given before surgery and sometimes after surgery. Ask your doctor why one is better than the other in your particular case.

If surgery, how does it impact outcomes?

Understanding what kind of surgery is needed and why is important. In addition, it's often helpful to udnerstand what the change in overall and progression free survival outcomes.

If radiation, which parts of the body?

It's helpful to understand how radiation might improve your odds at beating cancer, what the long-term effects are and where on the body is it going to be administered.

TREATMENT PLAN

TREATMENT INCLUDES

- ○ CHEMOTHERAPY
- ○ SURGERY
- ○ RADIATION
- ○ ____________________
- ○ HORMONE THERAPY
- ○ IMMUNE THERAPY
- ○ ____________________
- ○ ____________________

ORDER OF TREATMENT

- ☐ ____________________
- ☐ ____________________
- ☐ ____________________
- ☐ ____________________
- ☐ ____________________
- ☐ ____________________
- ☐ ____________________
- ☐ ____________________

WHAT IS STANDARD OF CARE?

ARE THERE ANY RELEVANT CLINICAL TRIALS?

DETAILS OF TREATMENT #1

TREATMENT NAME

TREATMENT DURATION

TREATMENT ALTERNATIVES (IF ANY)

TREATMENT SIDE EFFECTS (SHORT TERM)

TREATMENT SIDE EFFECTS (LONG TERM)

TREATMENT COSTS

DETAILS OF TREATMENT #2

TREATMENT NAME

TREATMENT DURATION

TREATMENT ALTERNATIVES (IF ANY)

TREATMENT SIDE EFFECTS (SHORT TERM)

TREATMENT SIDE EFFECTS (LONG TERM)

TREATMENT COSTS

See decision making tools on pg. 32

DETAILS OF TREATMENT #3

TREATMENT NAME

TREATMENT DURATION

TREATMENT ALTERNATIVES (IF ANY)

TREATMENT SIDE EFFECTS (SHORT TERM)

TREATMENT SIDE EFFECTS (LONG TERM)

TREATMENT COSTS

DETAILS OF TREATMENT #4

TREATMENT NAME

TREATMENT DURATION

TREATMENT ALTERNATIVES (IF ANY)

TREATMENT SIDE EFFECTS (SHORT TERM)

TREATMENT SIDE EFFECTS (LONG TERM)

TREATMENT COSTS

DETAILS OF TREATMENT #5

TREATMENT NAME

TREATMENT DURATION

TREATMENT ALTERNATIVES (IF ANY)

TREATMENT SIDE EFFECTS (SHORT TERM)

TREATMENT SIDE EFFECTS (LONG TERM)

TREATMENT COSTS

DETAILS OF TREATMENT #6

TREATMENT NAME

TREATMENT DURATION

TREATMENT ALTERNATIVES (IF ANY)

TREATMENT SIDE EFFECTS (SHORT TERM)

TREATMENT SIDE EFFECTS (LONG TERM)

TREATMENT COSTS

DETAILS OF TREATMENT #7

TREATMENT NAME

TREATMENT DURATION

TREATMENT ALTERNATIVES (IF ANY)

TREATMENT SIDE EFFECTS (SHORT TERM)

TREATMENT SIDE EFFECTS (LONG TERM)

TREATMENT COSTS

DETAILS OF TREATMENT #8

TREATMENT NAME

TREATMENT DURATION

TREATMENT ALTERNATIVES (IF ANY)

TREATMENT SIDE EFFECTS (SHORT TERM)

TREATMENT SIDE EFFECTS (LONG TERM)

TREATMENT COSTS

DECISION MAKING TOOL #1

BENEFITS OF THE TREATMENT

DETAILS

CONSEQUENCES OF THE TREATMENT

DETAILS

HOW YOU WANT TO LIVE YOUR LIFE

DETAILS

FINANCIAL IMPLICATIONS OF TREATMENT

DETAILS

DECISION MAKING TOOL #2

MOST AGGRESSIVE OPTION

OPTION	OPTION
DETAILS	DETAILS
ADVANTAGES	ADVANTAGES
DISADVANTAGES	DISADVANTAGES

LEAST AGGRESSIVE OPTION

OPTION	OPTION
DETAILS	DETAILS
ADVANTAGES	ADVANTAGES
DISADVANTAGES	DISADVANTAGES

SYMPTOM & NUTRITION PLAN

Cancer treatment often comes with a set of potential side-effects. While your care team can prepare you for some of them, your journey is unique, and thereby, your side effects are unique to you. Symptom tracking and active management has shown to improve quality of life during cancer treatment as well as overall outcomes of treatment.

Symptom management is often a complex array of medication, natural remedies, nutrition management and your own faith & belief based interventions. This chapter of the planner provides a simple structure to capture the methods of symptom management that you want to engage in.

SUPPORTIVE MEDICATION

Symptom management often includes additional medications to help with the side-effects of treatment.

NATURAL ALTERNATIVES

Often there are natural alternatives that have proven to be effective against some of the side effects. For e..g, prune juice for constipation.

SYMPTOM MANAGEMENT PLAN

LIST THE EXPECTED SYMPTOMS & HOW TO MANAGE THEM

SYMPTOM NAME:

SUPPORTIVE MEDICATION

NATURAL ALTERNATIVE

WHEN TO CALL YOUR CARE TEAM

SYMPTOM NAME:

SUPPORTIVE MEDICATION

NATURAL ALTERNATIVE

WHEN TO CALL YOUR CARE TEAM

SYMPTOM NAME:

SUPPORTIVE MEDICATION

NATURAL ALTERNATIVE

WHEN TO CALL YOUR CARE TEAM

SYMPTOM NAME:

SUPPORTIVE MEDICATION

NATURAL ALTERNATIVE

WHEN TO CALL YOUR CARE TEAM

SYMPTOM NAME:

SUPPORTIVE MEDICATION

NATURAL ALTERNATIVE

WHEN TO CALL YOUR CARE TEAM

SYMPTOM NAME:

SUPPORTIVE MEDICATION

NATURAL ALTERNATIVE

WHEN TO CALL YOUR CARE TEAM

SYMPTOM NAME:

SUPPORTIVE MEDICATION

NATURAL ALTERNATIVE

WHEN TO CALL YOUR CARE TEAM

SYMPTOM NAME:

SUPPORTIVE MEDICATION

NATURAL ALTERNATIVE

WHEN TO CALL YOUR CARE TEAM

SYMPTOM NAME:

SUPPORTIVE MEDICATION

NATURAL ALTERNATIVE

WHEN TO CALL YOUR CARE TEAM

SYMPTOM NAME:

SUPPORTIVE MEDICATION

NATURAL ALTERNATIVE

WHEN TO CALL YOUR CARE TEAM

SYMPTOM NAME:

SUPPORTIVE MEDICATION

NATURAL ALTERNATIVE

WHEN TO CALL YOUR CARE TEAM

SYMPTOM NAME:

SUPPORTIVE MEDICATION

NATURAL ALTERNATIVE

WHEN TO CALL YOUR CARE TEAM

NUTRITION PLAN

CHECK IF THERE ARE SPECIFIC FOODS TO EAT/AVOID

ANIMAL PRODUCTS (INCL. DAIRY)

SEAFOOD

RAW VEGETABLES & FRUITS

NUTS, BEANS, LENTILS

SOY PRODUCTS

PROCESSED & SPICY FOODS

WHAT ARE SOME FOODS THAT CAN HELP YOUR TREATMENT?

TYPE OF FOOD	BENEFITS

WHAT ARE SOME FOODS THAT SHOULD BE AVOIDED?

TYPE OF FOOD	HARMFUL BECAUSE

SUPPLEMENTS

ARE THERE SPECIFIC SUPPLEMENTS THAT SHOULD BE TAKEN?

SUPPLEMENT NAME	BENEFITS? RISKS?

HEALING PLAN

Cancer diagnosis and treatment can be so overwhelming that it's often easy to forget to remember to heal—physically, emotionally, and spiritually. There are a number of activities that one can engage in. These can include meditation, acupuncture, yoga, walking, mindfulness-based stress reduction, reiki and many others.

As with the rest of this planner, this really is your journey. This chapter provides space to capture your activities with the intention of healing your mind, body and soul.

This chapter also includes a few blank pages to draw, sketch, or write just for yourself.

SUGGESTIONS FOR HEALING

Acupuncture | Chiropractic Therapy | Massage Therapy | Meditation | Walks | Swimming | Reiki | Art | Music | Support Groups | Reading | Strength training | Healthy Eating | Breath work | Neurofeedback | Writing |

MIND
This can include meditation, mindfulness, therapy, support groups etc.

BODY
This can include yoga, tai-chi, mindful walking, massage, acupuncture etc.

SOUL
This includes anything that enables your soul to process this journey and evolve from it.

HEALING PLAN

HEALING ACTIVITY:

MY MOTIVATION

WHEN

WITH WHOM

HEALING ACTIVITY:

MY MOTIVATION

WHEN

WITH WHOM

HEALING ACTIVITY:

MY MOTIVATION

WHEN

WITH WHOM

HEALING ACTIVITY:

MY MOTIVATION

WHEN

WITH WHOM

HEALING ACTIVITY:

MY MOTIVATION

WHEN

WITH WHOM

HEALING ACTIVITY:

MY MOTIVATION

WHEN

WITH WHOM

HEALING ACTIVITY:

MY MOTIVATION

WHEN

WITH WHOM

HEALING ACTIVITY:

MY MOTIVATION

WHEN

WITH WHOM

YOUR SPACE

YOUR SPACE

YOUR SPACE

YOUR SPACE

DAILY CHECK IN

This section of the planner is meant for you to check-in with yourself regularly throughout this unique journey. It draws upon a body of cancer research that suggests capturing your daily symptoms can improve the outcome of your treatment. This is because it can help you recall detailed information that your care team relies on to modify and personalize your treatment. It also can help you know what to expect based on your own habits.

Additionally, it is designed to include practices from both western and eastern psychology that enables checking in with your body, mind and soul.

SYMPTOMS

This section includes space to capture your symptoms on an ongoing basis.

GRATITUDE & HOPE

This section provides space to capture what you are grateful for, anything you are excited about and a place for reflection.

NUTRITION & MEDS

This section provides space to capture any medications, acitivities or interventions that you are engaging in.

DAILY CHECK IN

DAY #	DATE	TREATMENT PHASE

I'M GRATEFUL FOR...

01 ....

....

02 ....

....

03 ....

....

I'M EXCITED FOR...

01 ....

....

02 ....

....

03 ....

....

HOW DO YOU FEEL?

HOW DID YOU SLEEP?

HOW WILL YOU EXCERCISE?

....

....

....

....

....

HOW WILL YOU HEAL?

....

....

....

....

....

SYMPTOM TRACKER

SYMPTOM	HOW BAD IS IT? 1	2	3	INTERVENTION
☐ *Fatigue*	○	○	○	
☐	○	○	○	
☐	○	○	○	
☐	○	○	○	
☐	○	○	○	
☐	○	○	○	
☐	○	○	○	

MEDICATION & NUTRITION TRACKER

MORNING

HYDRATE

NIGHT

NOTES FOR CARE TEAM:

DAILY CHECK IN

DAY #	DATE	TREATMENT PHASE

I'M GRATEFUL FOR...

01 ....

....

02 ....

....

03 ....

....

I'M EXCITED FOR...

01 ....

....

02 ....

....

03 ....

....

HOW DO YOU FEEL?

HOW DID YOU SLEEP?

HOW WILL YOU EXCERCISE?

....

....

....

....

....

HOW WILL YOU HEAL?

....

....

....

....

....

SYMPTOM TRACKER

SYMPTOM	HOW BAD IS IT? 1	2	3	INTERVENTION
☐ *Fatigue*	○	○	○	
☐	○	○	○	
☐	○	○	○	
☐	○	○	○	
☐	○	○	○	
☐	○	○	○	
☐	○	○	○	

MEDICATION & NUTRITION TRACKER

MORNING

HYDRATE

NIGHT

NOTES FOR CARE TEAM:

DAILY CHECK IN

DAY #	DATE	TREATMENT PHASE

I'M GRATEFUL FOR...

01 ....

....

02 ....

....

03 ....

....

I'M EXCITED FOR...

01 ....

....

02 ....

....

03 ....

....

HOW DO YOU FEEL?

HOW DID YOU SLEEP?

HOW WILL YOU EXCERCISE?

....

....

....

....

....

HOW WILL YOU HEAL?

....

....

....

....

....

SYMPTOM TRACKER

SYMPTOM	HOW BAD IS IT? 1	2	3	INTERVENTION
☐ *Fatigue*	○	○	○	
☐ ________	○	○	○	
☐ ________	○	○	○	
☐ ________	○	○	○	
☐ ________	○	○	○	
☐ ________	○	○	○	
☐ ________	○	○	○	

MEDICATION & NUTRITION TRACKER

MORNING

HYDRATE

NIGHT

NOTES FOR CARE TEAM:

DAILY CHECK IN

DAY #	DATE	TREATMENT PHASE

I'M GRATEFUL FOR...

01 ....

....

02 ....

....

03 ....

....

I'M EXCITED FOR...

01 ....

....

02 ....

....

03 ....

....

HOW DO YOU FEEL?

HOW DID YOU SLEEP?

HOW WILL YOU EXCERCISE?

....

....

....

....

....

HOW WILL YOU HEAL?

....

....

....

....

....

SYMPTOM TRACKER

SYMPTOM	HOW BAD IS IT? 1	2	3	INTERVENTION
☐ *Fatigue*	○	○	○	....
☐ ________	○	○	○	....
☐ ________	○	○	○	....
☐ ________	○	○	○	....
☐ ________	○	○	○	....
☐ ________	○	○	○	....
☐ ________	○	○	○	....

MEDICATION & NUTRITION TRACKER

MORNING

HYDRATE

NIGHT

NOTES FOR CARE TEAM:

DAILY CHECK IN

DAY #	DATE	TREATMENT PHASE

I'M GRATEFUL FOR...

01 ....

....

02 ....

....

03 ....

....

I'M EXCITED FOR...

01 ....

....

02 ....

....

03 ....

....

HOW DO YOU FEEL?

HOW DID YOU SLEEP?

HOW WILL YOU EXCERCISE?

....

....

....

....

....

HOW WILL YOU HEAL?

....

....

....

....

....

SYMPTOM TRACKER

SYMPTOM	HOW BAD IS IT? 1	2	3	INTERVENTION
☐ *Fatigue*	○	○	○	....
☐ ________	○	○	○	....
☐ ________	○	○	○	....
☐ ________	○	○	○	....
☐ ________	○	○	○	....
☐ ________	○	○	○	....
☐ ________	○	○	○	....

MEDICATION & NUTRITION TRACKER

MORNING

HYDRATE

NIGHT

NOTES FOR CARE TEAM:

DAILY CHECK IN

DAY #	DATE	TREATMENT PHASE

I'M GRATEFUL FOR...

01 ....

....

02 ....

....

03 ....

....

I'M EXCITED FOR...

01 ....

....

02 ....

....

03 ....

....

HOW DO YOU FEEL?

HOW DID YOU SLEEP?

HOW WILL YOU EXCERCISE?

....

....

....

....

....

HOW WILL YOU HEAL?

....

....

....

....

....

SYMPTOM TRACKER

SYMPTOM	HOW BAD IS IT? 1	2	3	INTERVENTION
☐ *Fatigue*	○	○	○	
☐	○	○	○	
☐	○	○	○	
☐	○	○	○	
☐	○	○	○	
☐	○	○	○	
☐	○	○	○	

MEDICATION & NUTRITION TRACKER

MORNING

HYDRATE

NIGHT

NOTES FOR CARE TEAM:

DAILY CHECK IN

DAY #	DATE	TREATMENT PHASE

I'M GRATEFUL FOR...

01 ....

....

02 ....

....

03 ....

....

I'M EXCITED FOR...

01 ....

....

02 ....

....

03 ....

....

HOW DO YOU FEEL?

HOW DID YOU SLEEP?

HOW WILL YOU EXCERCISE?

....

....

....

....

....

HOW WILL YOU HEAL?

....

....

....

....

....

SYMPTOM TRACKER

SYMPTOM	HOW BAD IS IT? 1	2	3	INTERVENTION
☐ *Fatigue*	○	○	○	
☐	○	○	○	
☐	○	○	○	
☐	○	○	○	
☐	○	○	○	
☐	○	○	○	
☐	○	○	○	

MEDICATION & NUTRITION TRACKER

MORNING

HYDRATE

NIGHT

NOTES FOR CARE TEAM:

DAILY CHECK IN

DAY #	DATE	TREATMENT PHASE

I'M GRATEFUL FOR...

01 ....

....

02 ....

....

03 ....

....

I'M EXCITED FOR...

01 ....

....

02 ....

....

03 ....

....

HOW DO YOU FEEL?

HOW DID YOU SLEEP?

HOW WILL YOU EXCERCISE?

....

....

....

....

....

HOW WILL YOU HEAL?

....

....

....

....

....

SYMPTOM TRACKER

SYMPTOM	HOW BAD IS IT? 1	2	3	INTERVENTION
☐ *Fatigue*	○	○	○	....
☐ ________	○	○	○	....
☐ ________	○	○	○	....
☐ ________	○	○	○	....
☐ ________	○	○	○	....
☐ ________	○	○	○	....
☐ ________	○	○	○	....

MEDICATION & NUTRITION TRACKER

MORNING

HYDRATE

NIGHT

NOTES FOR CARE TEAM:

DAILY CHECK IN

DAY #	DATE	TREATMENT PHASE

I'M GRATEFUL FOR...

01 ....

....

02 ....

....

03 ....

....

I'M EXCITED FOR...

01 ....

....

02 ....

....

03 ....

....

HOW DO YOU FEEL?

HOW DID YOU SLEEP?

HOW WILL YOU EXCERCISE?

....

....

....

....

....

HOW WILL YOU HEAL?

....

....

....

....

....

SYMPTOM TRACKER

SYMPTOM	HOW BAD IS IT? 1	2	3	INTERVENTION
☐ *Fatigue*	○	○	○	
☐	○	○	○	
☐	○	○	○	
☐	○	○	○	
☐	○	○	○	
☐	○	○	○	
☐	○	○	○	

MEDICATION & NUTRITION TRACKER

MORNING

HYDRATE

NIGHT

NOTES FOR CARE TEAM:

DAILY CHECK IN

DAY #	DATE	TREATMENT PHASE

I'M GRATEFUL FOR...

01 ....

....

02 ....

....

03 ....

....

I'M EXCITED FOR...

01 ....

....

02 ....

....

03 ....

....

HOW DO YOU FEEL?

HOW DID YOU SLEEP?

HOW WILL YOU EXCERCISE?

....

....

....

....

....

HOW WILL YOU HEAL?

....

....

....

....

....

SYMPTOM TRACKER

SYMPTOM	HOW BAD IS IT? 1	2	3	INTERVENTION
☐ *Fatigue*	○	○	○	
☐	○	○	○	
☐	○	○	○	
☐	○	○	○	
☐	○	○	○	
☐	○	○	○	
☐	○	○	○	

MEDICATION & NUTRITION TRACKER

MORNING

HYDRATE

NIGHT

NOTES FOR CARE TEAM:

CAPTURE YOUR LEARNINGS

ESTABLISH YOUR NEW PATTERNS

MORNING

AFTERNOON

NIGHT

DAILY CHECK IN

DAY #	DATE	TREATMENT PHASE

I'M GRATEFUL FOR...

01 ....

....

02 ....

....

03 ....

....

I'M EXCITED FOR...

01 ....

....

02 ....

....

03 ....

....

HOW DO YOU FEEL?

HOW DID YOU SLEEP?

HOW WILL YOU EXCERCISE?

....

....

....

....

....

HOW WILL YOU HEAL?

....

....

....

....

....

SYMPTOM TRACKER

SYMPTOM	HOW BAD IS IT? 1	2	3	INTERVENTION
☐ *Fatigue*	○	○	○	
☐	○	○	○	
☐	○	○	○	
☐	○	○	○	
☐	○	○	○	
☐	○	○	○	
☐	○	○	○	

MEDICATION & NUTRITION TRACKER

MORNING

HYDRATE

NIGHT

NOTES FOR CARE TEAM:

DAILY CHECK IN

DAY #	DATE	TREATMENT PHASE

I'M GRATEFUL FOR...

01 ....

....

02 ....

....

03 ....

....

I'M EXCITED FOR...

01 ....

....

02 ....

....

03 ....

....

HOW DO YOU FEEL?

HOW DID YOU SLEEP?

HOW WILL YOU EXCERCISE?

....

....

....

....

....

HOW WILL YOU HEAL?

....

....

....

....

....

SYMPTOM TRACKER

SYMPTOM	HOW BAD IS IT? 1	2	3	INTERVENTION
☐ *Fatigue*	○	○	○	
☐	○	○	○	
☐	○	○	○	
☐	○	○	○	
☐	○	○	○	
☐	○	○	○	
☐	○	○	○	

MEDICATION & NUTRITION TRACKER

MORNING

HYDRATE

NIGHT

NOTES FOR CARE TEAM:

DAILY CHECK IN

DAY #	DATE	TREATMENT PHASE

I'M GRATEFUL FOR...

01 ....

....

02 ....

....

03 ....

....

I'M EXCITED FOR...

01 ....

....

02 ....

....

03 ....

....

HOW DO YOU FEEL?

HOW DID YOU SLEEP?

HOW WILL YOU EXCERCISE?

....

....

....

....

....

HOW WILL YOU HEAL?

....

....

....

....

....

SYMPTOM TRACKER

SYMPTOM	HOW BAD IS IT? 1	2	3	INTERVENTION
☐ *Fatigue*	○	○	○	....
☐ ________	○	○	○	....
☐ ________	○	○	○	....
☐ ________	○	○	○	....
☐ ________	○	○	○	....
☐ ________	○	○	○	....
☐ ________	○	○	○	....

MEDICATION & NUTRITION TRACKER

MORNING

HYDRATE

NIGHT

NOTES FOR CARE TEAM:

DAILY CHECK IN

DAY #	DATE	TREATMENT PHASE

I'M GRATEFUL FOR...

01 ....

....

02 ....

....

03 ....

....

I'M EXCITED FOR...

01 ....

....

02 ....

....

03 ....

....

HOW DO YOU FEEL?

HOW DID YOU SLEEP?

HOW WILL YOU EXCERCISE?

....

....

....

....

....

HOW WILL YOU HEAL?

....

....

....

....

....

SYMPTOM TRACKER

SYMPTOM	HOW BAD IS IT? 1	2	3	INTERVENTION
☐ *Fatigue*	○	○	○	
☐	○	○	○	
☐	○	○	○	
☐	○	○	○	
☐	○	○	○	
☐	○	○	○	
☐	○	○	○	

MEDICATION & NUTRITION TRACKER

MORNING

HYDRATE

NIGHT

NOTES FOR CARE TEAM:

DAILY CHECK IN

DAY #	DATE	TREATMENT PHASE

I'M GRATEFUL FOR...

01 ....

....

02 ....

....

03 ....

....

I'M EXCITED FOR...

01 ....

....

02 ....

....

03 ....

....

HOW DO YOU FEEL?

HOW DID YOU SLEEP?

HOW WILL YOU EXCERCISE?

....

....

....

....

....

HOW WILL YOU HEAL?

....

....

....

....

....

SYMPTOM TRACKER

SYMPTOM	HOW BAD IS IT? 1	2	3	INTERVENTION
☐ *Fatigue*	○	○	○	
☐	○	○	○	
☐	○	○	○	
☐	○	○	○	
☐	○	○	○	
☐	○	○	○	
☐	○	○	○	

MEDICATION & NUTRITION TRACKER

MORNING

HYDRATE

NIGHT

NOTES FOR CARE TEAM:

DAILY CHECK IN

DAY #	DATE	TREATMENT PHASE

I'M GRATEFUL FOR...

01 ....

....

02 ....

....

03 ....

....

I'M EXCITED FOR...

01 ....

....

02 ....

....

03 ....

....

HOW DO YOU FEEL?

HOW DID YOU SLEEP?

HOW WILL YOU EXCERCISE?

....

....

....

....

....

HOW WILL YOU HEAL?

....

....

....

....

....

SYMPTOM TRACKER

SYMPTOM	HOW BAD IS IT? 1	2	3	INTERVENTION
☐ *Fatigue*	○	○	○	
☐	○	○	○	
☐	○	○	○	
☐	○	○	○	
☐	○	○	○	
☐	○	○	○	
☐	○	○	○	

MEDICATION & NUTRITION TRACKER

MORNING

HYDRATE

NIGHT

NOTES FOR CARE TEAM:

DAILY CHECK IN

DAY #	DATE	TREATMENT PHASE

I'M GRATEFUL FOR...

01 ....

....

02 ....

....

03 ....

....

I'M EXCITED FOR...

01 ....

....

02 ....

....

03 ....

....

HOW DO YOU FEEL?

HOW DID YOU SLEEP?

HOW WILL YOU EXCERCISE?

....

....

....

....

....

HOW WILL YOU HEAL?

....

....

....

....

....

SYMPTOM TRACKER

SYMPTOM	HOW BAD IS IT? 1	2	3	INTERVENTION
☐ *Fatigue*	○	○	○	
☐	○	○	○	
☐	○	○	○	
☐	○	○	○	
☐	○	○	○	
☐	○	○	○	
☐	○	○	○	

MEDICATION & NUTRITION TRACKER

MORNING

HYDRATE

NIGHT

NOTES FOR CARE TEAM:

DAILY CHECK IN

DAY #	DATE	TREATMENT PHASE

I'M GRATEFUL FOR...

01 ....

....

02 ....

....

03 ....

....

I'M EXCITED FOR...

01 ....

....

02 ....

....

03 ....

....

HOW DO YOU FEEL?

HOW DID YOU SLEEP?

HOW WILL YOU EXCERCISE?

....

....

....

....

....

HOW WILL YOU HEAL?

....

....

....

....

....

SYMPTOM TRACKER

SYMPTOM	HOW BAD IS IT? 1	2	3	INTERVENTION
☐ *Fatigue*	○	○	○	....
☐ ________________	○	○	○	....
☐ ________________	○	○	○	....
☐ ________________	○	○	○	....
☐ ________________	○	○	○	....
☐ ________________	○	○	○	....
☐ ________________	○	○	○	....

MEDICATION & NUTRITION TRACKER

MORNING

HYDRATE

NIGHT

NOTES FOR CARE TEAM:

DAILY CHECK IN

DAY #	DATE	TREATMENT PHASE

I'M GRATEFUL FOR...

01 ....

....

02 ....

....

03 ....

....

I'M EXCITED FOR...

01 ....

....

02 ....

....

03 ....

....

HOW DO YOU FEEL?

HOW DID YOU SLEEP?

HOW WILL YOU EXCERCISE?

....

....

....

....

....

HOW WILL YOU HEAL?

....

....

....

....

....

SYMPTOM TRACKER

SYMPTOM	HOW BAD IS IT? 1	2	3	INTERVENTION
☐ *Fatigue*	○	○	○	
☐	○	○	○	
☐	○	○	○	
☐	○	○	○	
☐	○	○	○	
☐	○	○	○	
☐	○	○	○	

MEDICATION & NUTRITION TRACKER

MORNING

HYDRATE

NIGHT

NOTES FOR CARE TEAM:

CAPTURE YOUR LEARNINGS

ESTABLISH YOUR NEW PATTERNS

MORNING

AFTERNOON

NIGHT

DAILY CHECK IN

DAY #	DATE	TREATMENT PHASE

I'M GRATEFUL FOR...

01 ....

....

02 ....

....

03 ....

....

I'M EXCITED FOR...

01 ....

....

02 ....

....

03 ....

....

HOW DO YOU FEEL?

HOW DID YOU SLEEP?

HOW WILL YOU EXCERCISE?

....

....

....

....

....

HOW WILL YOU HEAL?

....

....

....

....

....

SYMPTOM TRACKER

SYMPTOM	HOW BAD IS IT? 1	2	3	INTERVENTION
☐ *Fatigue*	○	○	○	....
☐ ________	○	○	○	....
☐ ________	○	○	○	....
☐ ________	○	○	○	....
☐ ________	○	○	○	....
☐ ________	○	○	○	....
☐ ________	○	○	○	....

MEDICATION & NUTRITION TRACKER

MORNING

HYDRATE

NIGHT

NOTES FOR CARE TEAM:

DAILY CHECK IN

DAY #	DATE	TREATMENT PHASE

I'M GRATEFUL FOR...

01 ....

....

02 ....

....

03 ....

....

I'M EXCITED FOR...

01 ....

....

02 ....

....

03 ....

....

HOW DO YOU FEEL?

HOW DID YOU SLEEP?

HOW WILL YOU EXCERCISE?

....

....

....

....

....

HOW WILL YOU HEAL?

....

....

....

....

....

SYMPTOM TRACKER

SYMPTOM	HOW BAD IS IT? 1	2	3	INTERVENTION
☐ *Fatigue*	○	○	○	
☐	○	○	○	
☐	○	○	○	
☐	○	○	○	
☐	○	○	○	
☐	○	○	○	
☐	○	○	○	

MEDICATION & NUTRITION TRACKER

MORNING

HYDRATE

NIGHT

NOTES FOR CARE TEAM:

DAILY CHECK IN

DAY #	DATE	TREATMENT PHASE

I'M GRATEFUL FOR...

01 ....

....

02 ....

....

03 ....

....

I'M EXCITED FOR...

01 ....

....

02 ....

....

03 ....

....

HOW DO YOU FEEL?

HOW DID YOU SLEEP?

HOW WILL YOU EXCERCISE?

....

....

....

....

....

HOW WILL YOU HEAL?

....

....

....

....

....

SYMPTOM TRACKER

SYMPTOM	HOW BAD IS IT? 1	2	3	INTERVENTION
☐ *Fatigue*	○	○	○	
☐	○	○	○	
☐	○	○	○	
☐	○	○	○	
☐	○	○	○	
☐	○	○	○	
☐	○	○	○	

MEDICATION & NUTRITION TRACKER

MORNING

HYDRATE

NIGHT

NOTES FOR CARE TEAM:

DAILY CHECK IN

DAY #	DATE	TREATMENT PHASE

I'M GRATEFUL FOR...

01 ....

....

02 ....

....

03 ....

....

I'M EXCITED FOR...

01 ....

....

02 ....

....

03 ....

....

HOW DO YOU FEEL?

HOW DID YOU SLEEP?

HOW WILL YOU EXCERCISE?

....

....

....

....

....

HOW WILL YOU HEAL?

....

....

....

....

....

SYMPTOM TRACKER

SYMPTOM	HOW BAD IS IT? 1	2	3	INTERVENTION
☐ *Fatigue*	○	○	○	
☐	○	○	○	
☐	○	○	○	
☐	○	○	○	
☐	○	○	○	
☐	○	○	○	
☐	○	○	○	

MEDICATION & NUTRITION TRACKER

MORNING

HYDRATE

NIGHT

NOTES FOR CARE TEAM:

DAILY CHECK IN

DAY #	DATE	TREATMENT PHASE

I'M GRATEFUL FOR...

01 ....

....

02 ....

....

03 ....

....

I'M EXCITED FOR...

01 ....

....

02 ....

....

03 ....

....

HOW DO YOU FEEL?

HOW DID YOU SLEEP?

HOW WILL YOU EXCERCISE?

....

....

....

....

....

HOW WILL YOU HEAL?

....

....

....

....

....

SYMPTOM TRACKER

SYMPTOM	HOW BAD IS IT? 1	2	3	INTERVENTION
☐ *Fatigue*	○	○	○	
☐	○	○	○	
☐	○	○	○	
☐	○	○	○	
☐	○	○	○	
☐	○	○	○	
☐	○	○	○	

MEDICATION & NUTRITION TRACKER

MORNING

HYDRATE

NIGHT

NOTES FOR CARE TEAM:

DAILY CHECK IN

DAY #	DATE	TREATMENT PHASE

I'M GRATEFUL FOR...

01 ....

....

02 ....

....

03 ....

....

I'M EXCITED FOR...

01 ....

....

02 ....

....

03 ....

....

HOW DO YOU FEEL?

HOW DID YOU SLEEP?

HOW WILL YOU EXCERCISE?

....

....

....

....

....

HOW WILL YOU HEAL?

....

....

....

....

....

SYMPTOM TRACKER

SYMPTOM	HOW BAD IS IT? 1	2	3	INTERVENTION
☐ *Fatigue*	○	○	○	
☐	○	○	○	
☐	○	○	○	
☐	○	○	○	
☐	○	○	○	
☐	○	○	○	
☐	○	○	○	

MEDICATION & NUTRITION TRACKER

MORNING

HYDRATE

NIGHT

NOTES FOR CARE TEAM:

DAILY CHECK IN

DAY #	DATE	TREATMENT PHASE

I'M GRATEFUL FOR...

01

02

03

I'M EXCITED FOR...

01

02

03

HOW DO YOU FEEL?

HOW DID YOU SLEEP?

HOW WILL YOU EXCERCISE?

HOW WILL YOU HEAL?

SYMPTOM TRACKER

SYMPTOM	HOW BAD IS IT? 1	2	3	INTERVENTION
☐ *Fatigue*	○	○	○	
☐	○	○	○	
☐	○	○	○	
☐	○	○	○	
☐	○	○	○	
☐	○	○	○	
☐	○	○	○	

MEDICATION & NUTRITION TRACKER

MORNING

HYDRATE

NIGHT

NOTES FOR CARE TEAM:

DAILY CHECK IN

DAY #	DATE	TREATMENT PHASE

I'M GRATEFUL FOR...

01 ....

....

02 ....

....

03 ....

....

I'M EXCITED FOR...

01 ....

....

02 ....

....

03 ....

....

HOW DO YOU FEEL?

HOW DID YOU SLEEP?

HOW WILL YOU EXCERCISE?

....

....

....

....

....

HOW WILL YOU HEAL?

....

....

....

....

....

SYMPTOM TRACKER

SYMPTOM	HOW BAD IS IT? 1	2	3	INTERVENTION
☐ *Fatigue*	○	○	○	
☐ ____	○	○	○	
☐ ____	○	○	○	
☐ ____	○	○	○	
☐ ____	○	○	○	
☐ ____	○	○	○	
☐ ____	○	○	○	

MEDICATION & NUTRITION TRACKER

MORNING

HYDRATE

NIGHT

NOTES FOR CARE TEAM:

DAILY CHECK IN

DAY #	DATE	TREATMENT PHASE

I'M GRATEFUL FOR...

01

02

03

I'M EXCITED FOR...

01

02

03

HOW DO YOU FEEL?

HOW DID YOU SLEEP?

HOW WILL YOU EXCERCISE?

HOW WILL YOU HEAL?

SYMPTOM TRACKER

SYMPTOM	HOW BAD IS IT? 1	2	3	INTERVENTION
☐ *Fatigue*	○	○	○	....
☐ ________	○	○	○	....
☐ ________	○	○	○	....
☐ ________	○	○	○	....
☐ ________	○	○	○	....
☐ ________	○	○	○	....
☐ ________	○	○	○	....

MEDICATION & NUTRITION TRACKER

MORNING

HYDRATE

NIGHT

NOTES FOR CARE TEAM:

CAPTURE YOUR LEARNINGS

ESTABLISH YOUR NEW PATTERNS

MORNING

AFTERNOON

NIGHT

DAILY CHECK IN

DAY #	DATE	TREATMENT PHASE

I'M GRATEFUL FOR...

01 ....

....

02 ....

....

03 ....

....

I'M EXCITED FOR...

01 ....

....

02 ....

....

03 ....

....

HOW DO YOU FEEL?

HOW DID YOU SLEEP?

HOW WILL YOU EXCERCISE?

....

....

....

....

....

HOW WILL YOU HEAL?

....

....

....

....

....

SYMPTOM TRACKER

SYMPTOM	HOW BAD IS IT? 1	2	3	INTERVENTION
☐ *Fatigue*	○	○	○	
☐	○	○	○	
☐	○	○	○	
☐	○	○	○	
☐	○	○	○	
☐	○	○	○	
☐	○	○	○	

MEDICATION & NUTRITION TRACKER

MORNING

HYDRATE

NIGHT

NOTES FOR CARE TEAM:

DAILY CHECK IN

DAY #	DATE	TREATMENT PHASE

I'M GRATEFUL FOR...

01 ....

....

02 ....

....

03 ....

....

I'M EXCITED FOR...

01 ....

....

02 ....

....

03 ....

....

HOW DO YOU FEEL?

HOW DID YOU SLEEP?

HOW WILL YOU EXCERCISE?

....

....

....

....

....

HOW WILL YOU HEAL?

....

....

....

....

....

SYMPTOM TRACKER

SYMPTOM	HOW BAD IS IT? 1	2	3	INTERVENTION
☐ *Fatigue*	○	○	○	
☐	○	○	○	
☐	○	○	○	
☐	○	○	○	
☐	○	○	○	
☐	○	○	○	
☐	○	○	○	

MEDICATION & NUTRITION TRACKER

MORNING

HYDRATE

NIGHT

NOTES FOR CARE TEAM:

DAILY CHECK IN

DAY #	DATE	TREATMENT PHASE

I'M GRATEFUL FOR...

01 ....

....

02 ....

....

03 ....

....

I'M EXCITED FOR...

01 ....

....

02 ....

....

03 ....

....

HOW DO YOU FEEL?

HOW DID YOU SLEEP?

HOW WILL YOU EXCERCISE?

....

....

....

....

....

HOW WILL YOU HEAL?

....

....

....

....

....

SYMPTOM TRACKER

SYMPTOM	HOW BAD IS IT? 1	2	3	INTERVENTION
☐ *Fatigue*	○	○	○	
☐	○	○	○	
☐	○	○	○	
☐	○	○	○	
☐	○	○	○	
☐	○	○	○	
☐	○	○	○	

MEDICATION & NUTRITION TRACKER

MORNING

HYDRATE

NIGHT

NOTES FOR CARE TEAM:

DAILY CHECK IN

DAY #	DATE	TREATMENT PHASE

I'M GRATEFUL FOR...

01 ....

....

02 ....

....

03 ....

....

I'M EXCITED FOR...

01 ....

....

02 ....

....

03 ....

....

HOW DO YOU FEEL?

HOW DID YOU SLEEP?

HOW WILL YOU EXCERCISE?

....

....

....

....

....

HOW WILL YOU HEAL?

....

....

....

....

....

SYMPTOM TRACKER

SYMPTOM	HOW BAD IS IT? 1	2	3	INTERVENTION
☐ *Fatigue*	○	○	○	
☐	○	○	○	
☐	○	○	○	
☐	○	○	○	
☐	○	○	○	
☐	○	○	○	
☐	○	○	○	

MEDICATION & NUTRITION TRACKER

MORNING

HYDRATE

NIGHT

NOTES FOR CARE TEAM:

DAILY CHECK IN

DAY #	DATE	TREATMENT PHASE

I'M GRATEFUL FOR...

01 ....

....

02 ....

....

03 ....

....

I'M EXCITED FOR...

01 ....

....

02 ....

....

03 ....

....

HOW DO YOU FEEL?

HOW DID YOU SLEEP?

HOW WILL YOU EXCERCISE?

....

....

....

....

....

HOW WILL YOU HEAL?

....

....

....

....

....

SYMPTOM TRACKER

SYMPTOM	HOW BAD IS IT? 1	2	3	INTERVENTION
☐ *Fatigue*	○	○	○	....
☐ ________	○	○	○	....
☐ ________	○	○	○	....
☐ ________	○	○	○	....
☐ ________	○	○	○	....
☐ ________	○	○	○	....
☐ ________	○	○	○	....

MEDICATION & NUTRITION TRACKER

MORNING

HYDRATE

NIGHT

NOTES FOR CARE TEAM:

DAILY CHECK IN

DAY #	DATE	TREATMENT PHASE

I'M GRATEFUL FOR...

01 ....

....

02 ....

....

03 ....

....

I'M EXCITED FOR...

01 ....

....

02 ....

....

03 ....

....

HOW DO YOU FEEL?

HOW DID YOU SLEEP?

HOW WILL YOU EXCERCISE?

....

....

....

....

....

HOW WILL YOU HEAL?

....

....

....

....

....

SYMPTOM TRACKER

SYMPTOM	HOW BAD IS IT? 1	2	3	INTERVENTION
☐ *Fatigue*	○	○	○	
☐ ______	○	○	○	
☐ ______	○	○	○	
☐ ______	○	○	○	
☐ ______	○	○	○	
☐ ______	○	○	○	
☐ ______	○	○	○	

MEDICATION & NUTRITION TRACKER

MORNING

HYDRATE

NIGHT

NOTES FOR CARE TEAM:

DAILY CHECK IN

DAY #	DATE	TREATMENT PHASE

I'M GRATEFUL FOR...

01 ....

....

02 ....

....

03 ....

....

I'M EXCITED FOR...

01 ....

....

02 ....

....

03 ....

....

HOW DO YOU FEEL?

HOW DID YOU SLEEP?

HOW WILL YOU EXCERCISE?

....

....

....

....

....

HOW WILL YOU HEAL?

....

....

....

....

....

SYMPTOM TRACKER

SYMPTOM	HOW BAD IS IT? 1	2	3	INTERVENTION
☐ *Fatigue*	○	○	○	....
☐ ______	○	○	○	....
☐ ______	○	○	○	....
☐ ______	○	○	○	....
☐ ______	○	○	○	....
☐ ______	○	○	○	....
☐ ______	○	○	○	....

MEDICATION & NUTRITION TRACKER

MORNING

HYDRATE

NIGHT

NOTES FOR CARE TEAM:

DAILY CHECK IN

DAY #	DATE	TREATMENT PHASE

I'M GRATEFUL FOR...	I'M EXCITED FOR...
01	01
02	02
03	03

HOW DO YOU FEEL?

HOW DID YOU SLEEP?

HOW WILL YOU EXCERCISE?	HOW WILL YOU HEAL?

SYMPTOM TRACKER

SYMPTOM	HOW BAD IS IT? 1	2	3	INTERVENTION
☐ *Fatigue*	○	○	○	
☐ ____	○	○	○	
☐ ____	○	○	○	
☐ ____	○	○	○	
☐ ____	○	○	○	
☐ ____	○	○	○	
☐ ____	○	○	○	

MEDICATION & NUTRITION TRACKER

MORNING

HYDRATE

NIGHT

NOTES FOR CARE TEAM:

DAILY CHECK IN

DAY #	DATE	TREATMENT PHASE

I'M GRATEFUL FOR...

01 ....

....

02 ....

....

03 ....

....

I'M EXCITED FOR...

01 ....

....

02 ....

....

03 ....

....

HOW DO YOU FEEL?

HOW DID YOU SLEEP?

HOW WILL YOU EXCERCISE?

....

....

....

....

....

HOW WILL YOU HEAL?

....

....

....

....

....

SYMPTOM TRACKER

SYMPTOM	HOW BAD IS IT? 1	2	3	INTERVENTION
☐ *Fatigue*	○	○	○	....
☐ ______________	○	○	○	....
☐ ______________	○	○	○	....
☐ ______________	○	○	○	....
☐ ______________	○	○	○	....
☐ ______________	○	○	○	....
☐ ______________	○	○	○	....

MEDICATION & NUTRITION TRACKER

MORNING

HYDRATE

NIGHT

NOTES FOR CARE TEAM:

CAPTURE YOUR LEARNINGS

ESTABLISH YOUR NEW PATTERNS

MORNING

AFTERNOON

NIGHT

VISIT NOTES

This section allows you space to capture notes from your visit with your care team. Cancer related appointments can be overwhelming with a lot of information being shared. The information itself can be technical in nature, which is often hard to comprehend. The visits can also be emotionally intense as it pertains to your ability to live the life you desire.

This section is structured and provides space for you to write down your recent symptoms, capture your questions and document notes from your visit.

From my personal experience, the more detailed patients can be about the symptoms they are facing, and their questions, the better the doctors can help us!

VISIT NOTES

VISIT WITH

DAY	DATE	TREATMENT PHASE

QUESTIONS FOR YOUR CARE TEAM

SYMPTOMS TO REPORT

SYMPTOM			SEVERE	INTERVENTION
☐ Fatigue	○	○	○	
☐	○	○	○	
☐	○	○	○	
☐	○	○	○	
☐	○	○	○	
☐	○	○	○	
☐	○	○	○	

NOTES FROM THE VISIT

FOLLOW-UPS FROM THIS VISIT

VISIT NOTES

VISIT WITH

DAY	DATE	TREATMENT PHASE

QUESTIONS FOR YOUR CARE TEAM

SYMPTOMS TO REPORT

SYMPTOM			*SEVERE*	INTERVENTION
☐ Fatigue	○	○	○	
☐ ____________	○	○	○	
☐ ____________	○	○	○	
☐ ____________	○	○	○	
☐ ____________	○	○	○	
☐ ____________	○	○	○	
☐ ____________	○	○	○	

NOTES FROM THE VISIT

FOLLOW-UPS FROM THIS VISIT

VISIT NOTES

VISIT WITH

DAY	DATE	TREATMENT PHASE

QUESTIONS FOR YOUR CARE TEAM

SYMPTOMS TO REPORT

SYMPTOM			SEVERE	INTERVENTION
☐ Fatigue	○	○	○	
☐	○	○	○	
☐	○	○	○	
☐	○	○	○	
☐	○	○	○	
☐	○	○	○	
☐	○	○	○	

NOTES FROM THE VISIT

FOLLOW-UPS FROM THIS VISIT

VISIT NOTES

VISIT WITH

DAY	DATE	TREATMENT PHASE

QUESTIONS FOR YOUR CARE TEAM

SYMPTOMS TO REPORT

SYMPTOM			*SEVERE*	INTERVENTION
☐ Fatigue	○	○	○	....
☐ ______	○	○	○	....
☐ ______	○	○	○	....
☐ ______	○	○	○	....
☐ ______	○	○	○	....
☐ ______	○	○	○	....
☐ ______	○	○	○	....

NOTES FROM THE VISIT

FOLLOW-UPS FROM THIS VISIT

VISIT NOTES

VISIT WITH

DAY	DATE	TREATMENT PHASE

QUESTIONS FOR YOUR CARE TEAM

SYMPTOMS TO REPORT

SYMPTOM			SEVERE	INTERVENTION
☐ Fatigue	○	○	○	
☐ ______	○	○	○	
☐ ______	○	○	○	
☐ ______	○	○	○	
☐ ______	○	○	○	
☐ ______	○	○	○	
☐ ______	○	○	○	

NOTES FROM THE VISIT

FOLLOW-UPS FROM THIS VISIT

VISIT NOTES

VISIT WITH

DAY	DATE	TREATMENT PHASE

QUESTIONS FOR YOUR CARE TEAM

SYMPTOMS TO REPORT

SYMPTOM			SEVERE	INTERVENTION
☐ Fatigue	○	○	○	
☐	○	○	○	
☐	○	○	○	
☐	○	○	○	
☐	○	○	○	
☐	○	○	○	
☐	○	○	○	

NOTES FROM THE VISIT

FOLLOW-UPS FROM THIS VISIT

VISIT NOTES

VISIT WITH

DAY	DATE	TREATMENT PHASE

QUESTIONS FOR YOUR CARE TEAM

SYMPTOMS TO REPORT

SYMPTOM			*SEVERE*	INTERVENTION
☐ Fatigue	○	○	○	
☐	○	○	○	
☐	○	○	○	
☐	○	○	○	
☐	○	○	○	
☐	○	○	○	
☐	○	○	○	

NOTES FROM THE VISIT

FOLLOW-UPS FROM THIS VISIT

VISIT NOTES

VISIT WITH

DAY	DATE	TREATMENT PHASE

QUESTIONS FOR YOUR CARE TEAM

SYMPTOMS TO REPORT

SYMPTOM			*SEVERE*	INTERVENTION
☐ Fatigue	○	○	○	....
☐ ________	○	○	○	....
☐ ________	○	○	○	....
☐ ________	○	○	○	....
☐ ________	○	○	○	....
☐ ________	○	○	○	....
☐ ________	○	○	○	....

NOTES FROM THE VISIT

FOLLOW-UPS FROM THIS VISIT

VISIT NOTES

VISIT WITH

DAY	DATE	TREATMENT PHASE

QUESTIONS FOR YOUR CARE TEAM

SYMPTOMS TO REPORT

SYMPTOM			*SEVERE*	INTERVENTION
☐ Fatigue	○	○	○	
☐	○	○	○	
☐	○	○	○	
☐	○	○	○	
☐	○	○	○	
☐	○	○	○	
☐	○	○	○	

NOTES FROM THE VISIT

FOLLOW-UPS FROM THIS VISIT

VISIT NOTES

VISIT WITH

DAY	DATE	TREATMENT PHASE

QUESTIONS FOR YOUR CARE TEAM

SYMPTOMS TO REPORT

SYMPTOM			*SEVERE*	INTERVENTION
☐ Fatigue	○	○	○	....
☐ ____________________	○	○	○	....
☐ ____________________	○	○	○	....
☐ ____________________	○	○	○	....
☐ ____________________	○	○	○	....
☐ ____________________	○	○	○	....
☐ ____________________	○	○	○	....

NOTES FROM THE VISIT

FOLLOW-UPS FROM THIS VISIT

VISIT NOTES

VISIT WITH

DAY	DATE	TREATMENT PHASE

QUESTIONS FOR YOUR CARE TEAM

SYMPTOMS TO REPORT

SYMPTOM		SEVERE		INTERVENTION
☐ Fatigue	○	○	○	
☐	○	○	○	
☐	○	○	○	
☐	○	○	○	
☐	○	○	○	
☐	○	○	○	
☐	○	○	○	

NOTES FROM THE VISIT

FOLLOW-UPS FROM THIS VISIT

VISIT NOTES

VISIT WITH

DAY	DATE	TREATMENT PHASE

QUESTIONS FOR YOUR CARE TEAM

SYMPTOMS TO REPORT

SYMPTOM			SEVERE	INTERVENTION
☐ Fatigue	○	○	○	
☐ ______	○	○	○	
☐ ______	○	○	○	
☐ ______	○	○	○	
☐ ______	○	○	○	
☐ ______	○	○	○	
☐ ______	○	○	○	

NOTES FROM THE VISIT

FOLLOW-UPS FROM THIS VISIT

VISIT NOTES

VISIT WITH

DAY	DATE	TREATMENT PHASE

QUESTIONS FOR YOUR CARE TEAM

SYMPTOMS TO REPORT

SYMPTOM			*SEVERE*	INTERVENTION
☐ Fatigue	○	○	○	....
☐ ________	○	○	○	....
☐ ________	○	○	○	....
☐ ________	○	○	○	....
☐ ________	○	○	○	....
☐ ________	○	○	○	....
☐ ________	○	○	○	....

NOTES FROM THE VISIT

FOLLOW-UPS FROM THIS VISIT

VISIT NOTES

VISIT WITH

DAY	DATE	TREATMENT PHASE

QUESTIONS FOR YOUR CARE TEAM

SYMPTOMS TO REPORT

SYMPTOM			*SEVERE*	INTERVENTION
☐ Fatigue	○	○	○	....
☐ ________	○	○	○	....
☐ ________	○	○	○	....
☐ ________	○	○	○	....
☐ ________	○	○	○	....
☐ ________	○	○	○	....
☐ ________	○	○	○	....

NOTES FROM THE VISIT

FOLLOW-UPS FROM THIS VISIT

VISIT NOTES

VISIT WITH

DAY	DATE	TREATMENT PHASE

QUESTIONS FOR YOUR CARE TEAM

SYMPTOMS TO REPORT

SYMPTOM			*SEVERE*	INTERVENTION
☐ Fatigue	○	○	○	....
☐ ________	○	○	○	....
☐ ________	○	○	○	....
☐ ________	○	○	○	....
☐ ________	○	○	○	....
☐ ________	○	○	○	....
☐ ________	○	○	○	....

NOTES FROM THE VISIT

FOLLOW-UPS FROM THIS VISIT

VISIT NOTES

VISIT WITH

DAY	DATE	TREATMENT PHASE

QUESTIONS FOR YOUR CARE TEAM

SYMPTOMS TO REPORT

SYMPTOM			*SEVERE*	INTERVENTION
☐ Fatigue	○	○	○	
☐ ______	○	○	○	
☐ ______	○	○	○	
☐ ______	○	○	○	
☐ ______	○	○	○	
☐ ______	○	○	○	
☐ ______	○	○	○	

NOTES FROM THE VISIT

FOLLOW-UPS FROM THIS VISIT

VISIT NOTES

VISIT WITH

DAY	DATE	TREATMENT PHASE

QUESTIONS FOR YOUR CARE TEAM

SYMPTOMS TO REPORT

SYMPTOM		SEVERE		INTERVENTION
☐ Fatigue	○	○	○	
☐	○	○	○	
☐	○	○	○	
☐	○	○	○	
☐	○	○	○	
☐	○	○	○	
☐	○	○	○	

NOTES FROM THE VISIT

FOLLOW-UPS FROM THIS VISIT

VISIT NOTES

VISIT WITH

DAY	DATE	TREATMENT PHASE

QUESTIONS FOR YOUR CARE TEAM

SYMPTOMS TO REPORT

SYMPTOM			*SEVERE*	INTERVENTION
☐ Fatigue	○	○	○	
☐ ______	○	○	○	
☐ ______	○	○	○	
☐ ______	○	○	○	
☐ ______	○	○	○	
☐ ______	○	○	○	
☐ ______	○	○	○	

NOTES FROM THE VISIT

FOLLOW-UPS FROM THIS VISIT

VISIT NOTES

VISIT WITH

DAY	DATE	TREATMENT PHASE

QUESTIONS FOR YOUR CARE TEAM

SYMPTOMS TO REPORT

SYMPTOM			*SEVERE*	INTERVENTION
☐ Fatigue	○	○	○	....
☐ ____________	○	○	○	....
☐ ____________	○	○	○	....
☐ ____________	○	○	○	....
☐ ____________	○	○	○	....
☐ ____________	○	○	○	....
☐ ____________	○	○	○	....

NOTES FROM THE VISIT

FOLLOW-UPS FROM THIS VISIT

VISIT NOTES

VISIT WITH

DAY	DATE	TREATMENT PHASE

QUESTIONS FOR YOUR CARE TEAM

SYMPTOMS TO REPORT

SYMPTOM			*SEVERE*	INTERVENTION
☐ Fatigue	○	○	○	
☐	○	○	○	
☐	○	○	○	
☐	○	○	○	
☐	○	○	○	
☐	○	○	○	
☐	○	○	○	

NOTES FROM THE VISIT

FOLLOW-UPS FROM THIS VISIT

VISIT NOTES

VISIT WITH

DAY	DATE	TREATMENT PHASE

QUESTIONS FOR YOUR CARE TEAM

SYMPTOMS TO REPORT

SYMPTOM			*SEVERE*	INTERVENTION
☐ Fatigue	○	○	○	....
☐ ______	○	○	○	....
☐ ______	○	○	○	....
☐ ______	○	○	○	....
☐ ______	○	○	○	....
☐ ______	○	○	○	....
☐ ______	○	○	○	....

NOTES FROM THE VISIT

FOLLOW-UPS FROM THIS VISIT

VISIT NOTES

VISIT WITH

DAY	DATE	TREATMENT PHASE

QUESTIONS FOR YOUR CARE TEAM

SYMPTOMS TO REPORT

SYMPTOM			*SEVERE*	INTERVENTION
☐ Fatigue	○	○	○	
☐ ______	○	○	○	
☐ ______	○	○	○	
☐ ______	○	○	○	
☐ ______	○	○	○	
☐ ______	○	○	○	
☐ ______	○	○	○	

NOTES FROM THE VISIT

FOLLOW-UPS FROM THIS VISIT

VISIT NOTES

VISIT WITH

DAY	DATE	TREATMENT PHASE

QUESTIONS FOR YOUR CARE TEAM

SYMPTOMS TO REPORT				
SYMPTOM			*SEVERE*	INTERVENTION
☐ Fatigue	○	○	○	....
☐ ______	○	○	○	....
☐ ______	○	○	○	....
☐ ______	○	○	○	....
☐ ______	○	○	○	....
☐ ______	○	○	○	....
☐ ______	○	○	○	....

NOTES FROM THE VISIT

FOLLOW-UPS FROM THIS VISIT

VISIT NOTES

VISIT WITH

DAY	DATE	TREATMENT PHASE

QUESTIONS FOR YOUR CARE TEAM

SYMPTOMS TO REPORT

SYMPTOM			*SEVERE*	INTERVENTION
☐ Fatigue	○	○	○	
☐	○	○	○	
☐	○	○	○	
☐	○	○	○	
☐	○	○	○	
☐	○	○	○	
☐	○	○	○	

NOTES FROM THE VISIT

FOLLOW-UPS FROM THIS VISIT

RESEARCH NOTES

NOTES

p. 184

NOTES

NOTES

NOTES

NOTES

NOTES

NOTES

NOTES

MANTA PLANNER

Learn how to best use this treatment planner on our website and access specific content on managing treatment for cancer. Visit us at

www.mantaplanner.com

Lightning Source UK Ltd.
Milton Keynes UK
UKHW010822031022
409835UK00003B/521